In the Attic

Lalie Harcourt & Ricki Wortzman

Illustrated by Vesna Krstanovic

gagelearning

In the house there is
an attic.

In the attic there is
a trunk.

In the trunk there are
some drawers.

In the drawers there are
some boxes.

In the boxes there are
some clothes.

In the clothes there are
some pockets.

In the attic there is a play.